WHY INDIE?

At Independent Oxford and Bitten Oxford, we love our independent shops and eateries. We are passionate about singing the praises of Oxford's indies and want the Compendium to fuel your travels around our city.

But why shop indie? By shopping independent you're supporting craftspeople, experts in their fields and people who care absolutely 100% about what they're doing and why they're doing what they do. What you get from an indie, we know wholeheartedly, is more genuine.

Next time you go into an indie, ask them about their products and what they do. An indie business owner will have an in-depth knowledge of their product and delight in telling you more. We're sure it will bring a new meaning and enjoyment to shopping and eating local!

There's something magical about your favourite cafe remembering your daily coffee order or your favourite shop gift wrapping that special present.

Finally, shopping and eating local means you're actively supporting someone's livelihood and their family, as well as the local economy. We thrive on relationships and happy communities, and by shopping local you're fuelling exactly this, one purchase at a time.

We hope the Indie Oxford Compendium inspires you to shop local, eat local, and discover the stories behind the independents.

Start exploring and keep in touch!

#OxCompendium

WHEN YOU BUY FROM
A SMALL BUSINESS,
AN ACTUAL PERSON
DOES A LITTLE
HAPPY DANCE

CONTENTS

COLOUR KEY

RESTAURANTS, CAFES & BARS

RETAIL

HOTELS & GUESTHOUSES

INDIE PEOPLE

INDIE EVENTS

Oxford's Food & Drink Guide

Becca and Jacqui bonded over burgers back in 2013 and from that meal grew the idea of Bitten Oxford, a website providing listings of all places to eat in Oxford, news and information about local food and drink, and genuinely honest reviews, sometimes brutally honest.

From that, another conversation along the lines of "Ooh, we could do that!" led to the start of Bitten Street, a monthly street food event held at the Oxford Castle. Listed by the Daily Telegraph as one of the Top Ten UK Street Food Events and also recommended by the Guardian, Bitten Street quickly became a fixture on the Oxford food scene. Regular local food traders with a few changing traders from further afield, a Bitten Bar with local beers and ciders, and a DJ create a destination where you're guaranteed amazing food and drink.

Then we decided Oxford really needed its own food and drink festival that was different in that it would only have businesses from within Oxfordshire. In October 2016, the inaugural festival was held and we're now in the process of planning for autumn 2017.

All this while balancing children, pets, husbands and a full time job! There's a lot of online chats, phone calls and meetings, so much so that we now refer to each other as the work wife! We love what we do and have met some amazing people in Oxford and through this Compendium, and we hope you will too.

bittenoxford.com

 BITTENOXFORD　　 BITTENOXFORD　　 BITTENOXFORD

4

Independent Oxford was founded by us, Anna Munday & Rosie Jacobs, in 2015 and is dedicated to unearthing the plethora of Oxford's great independents.

After meeting at Wilderness Festival and discovering a shared passion for independent shops, we embarked on making indie stores and eateries more visible to Oxford locals and tourists alike.

First came the launch of the website, a constantly evolving online directory of independents in the city, in March 2015. The overwhelming enthusiasm received for the project quickly led us onto a regular blog, pop-up mini-markets and Oxford's first fully independent Christmas Market eight months later at Turl Street Kitchen. Collaborative Instameets have also become a firm fixture of our Independent Oxford calendar!

As well as singing the praises of independents to the public, we both wanted Independent Oxford to create a community so that indie business owners could collaborate, discuss ideas and form a group that could work together to support and promote each other. By working together, independents in Oxford have a voice that is much more likely to be heard above the buzz of high street chains and big corporations.

Now, two years in, we have a business membership scheme, are planning our third Christmas Market in December 2017, and we are proud to be working on the Compendium with Bitten Oxford.

Tag your indie finds with #IndieOxford
independentoxford.com

 INDEPENDENTOXFORD    INDIEOXFORD    INDEPENDENTOXFORD

HUG A SMALL BUSINESS
OWNER TODAY
- OR AT LEAST BUY
FROM THEM

OX1

CENTRAL AND SOUTH OXFORD

The heart of our city stretches from the High Street to the train station, and from St. Aldates to St. Giles, the site of the famous fair for over 200 years. Known for its dreaming spires and gowned students, our beautiful city is so much more with its vast array of independents. Book a stay in an independent hotel and stroll through the city to discover market traders, boutiques, quirky hidden cafés and exceptional restaurants.

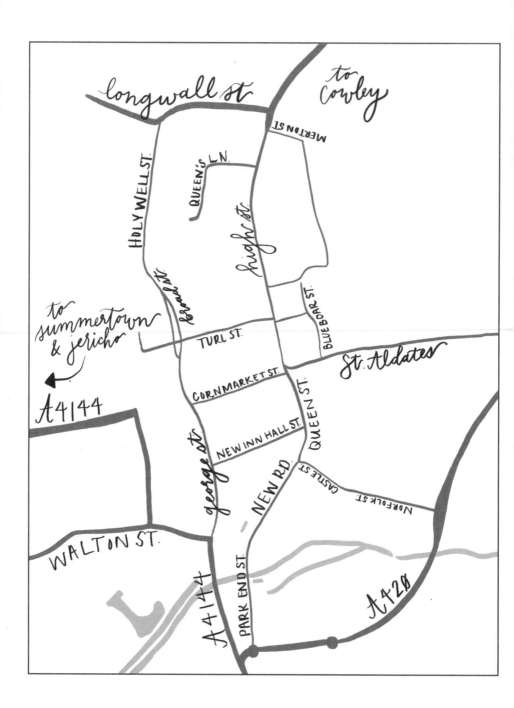

A contemporary bar with a strong focus on wines, craft beer and good spirits. Our cheese and charcuterie menu is developed to complement our drinks and is of the highest quality. All this with a great team and a relaxed atmosphere makes us stand out from the rest.

WHY WE LOVE IT: GREAT PLACE TO MEET FOR A FEW DRINKS AND WORK YOUR WAY THROUGH THE WINE LIST!

ADDRESS: 4 OXFORD CASTLE, NEW ROAD, OXFORD OX1 1AY
TELEPHONE: 01865 247217
WEBSITE: 1855OXFORD.COM

 1855OXFORD    1855OXFORD    1855OXFORD

ASPIRE STYLE

Discover something unique. Vintage inspired fashion & gifts to aspire to. Aspire specialises in unique and independent labels for women who love beautiful dresses, unusual jewellery, handbags and fabulous gifts. We also do a range of engraved jewellery from £15 that can be personalised while you wait.

WHY WE LOVE IT: A GREAT PLACE TO FIND UNUSUAL CLOTHING BRANDS AND A WHOLE HOST OF PRETTY GIFTS.

ADDRESS: 21 HIGH STREET, OXFORD OX1 4AH
TELEPHONE: 01865 202600
WEBSITE: ASPIRESTYLE.CO.UK

 ASPIRESTYLE    ASPIRESTYLE

Babylon specialises in eclectic, exceptional & unique home interiors and giftware, all cherry picked to create an individual style. There's a choice of sublime ranges of unique, reclaimed furniture, stylish mirrors & lighting, beautiful handmade silver jewellery, luxurious home textiles and wonderful gift ideas.

WHY WE LOVE IT: A LOVELY FAMILY RUN STORE FOR FINDING QUIRKY AND DIFFERENT PIECES FOR THE HOME.

ADDRESS: 86/87 HIGH STREET, OXFORD OX1 4BG
TELEPHONE: 01865 245577
WEBSITE: BABYLONTRADING.CO.UK

 BABYLONTRADING    BABYLON_TRADING

BONNERS

An independent, traditional and family run fruit and vegetable supplier. We are based in the heart of Oxford at The Covered Market. Bonners offers a wide range of fruit and vegetables, spices, dried fruits and nuts.

WHY WE LOVE IT: THESE GUYS KNOW THEIR FRUIT & VEG! A GREAT PLACE TO FIND SEASONAL PRODUCE & GET SOME RECIPE INSPIRATION TOO.

ADDRESS: 16, 20 & 49, THE COVERED MARKET, OXFORD OX1 3DU
TELEPHONE: 01865 242183
WEBSITE:

Boswells is the oldest family owned department store in the world and has been trading in Oxford since 1738. Spread over 4 floors, we specialise in cookware, gifts, linens, luggage, cosmetics, pharmacy and toys. The store also has the 1738 Tea Room Café on the 1st floor. Come for lunch or a traditional afternoon tea.

WHY WE LOVE IT: NEED SOMETHING FOR THE HOME OR KITCHEN AND NOT SURE WHERE TO FIND IT? BOSWELLS IS THE ANSWER! WE LOVE OXFORD'S OLDEST DEPARTMENT STORE.

ADDRESS: 1-4 BROAD STREET , OXFORD OX1 3AG
TELEPHONE: 01865 241244
WEBSITE: BOSWELLS.CO.UK

 BOSWELLSOFOXFORD    BOSWELLSOXFORD    BOSWELLSOXFORD

BROAD CANVAS

Oxfordshire's premier independent art and craft supplies shop caters for artists (amateur and professional) as well as hobbyists, craftspeople and students. Staffed by practicing artists with a wide knowledge base, we aim to support your creativity by offering sound advice and quality materials. A treasure trove of inspiration.

WHY WE LOVE IT: REQUIRE ART AND CRAFT SUPPLIES? THEN BROAD CANVAS IS A GOLD MINE THAT'S STARTED MANY AN ARTISTIC CAREER (OR HOBBY!)

ADDRESS: 20 BROAD STREET, OXFORD OX1 3AS
TELEPHONE: 01865 244025
WEBSITE: BROADCANVAS.NET

 BROADCANVAS
 BROADCANVASLTD
 BROADCANVASOXFORD

We are a specialist men's boutique curating the best products by specialist craftsmen from the UK and around the world bringing the best of fashion gifts, accessories and grooming needs for every discerning gentleman.

WHY WE LOVE IT: EXPERTLY PICKED GIFTS AND ATTIRE FOR MEN WITH FRIENDLY SERVICE TO BOOT!

ADDRESS: 31 THE MARKET, OXFORD OX1 3DU
TELEPHONE: 01865 243412
WEBSITE: BURROWSANDHARE.CO.UK

 BURROWS&HARE    BURROWS_HARE    BURROWS_AND_HARE

COLOMBIA COFFEE ROASTERS

We are a generation of coffee growers in Columbia and speciality coffee micro roasters based in Oxford. Located in the Covered Market, join us for a coffee and one of our carefully selected cakes.

WHY WE LOVE IT: GREAT PLACE TO SIT AND WATCH THE COMINGS AND GOINGS OF THE COVERED MARKET. EVEN BETTER WITH A BEN'S COOKIE!

ADDRESS: 106-107 THE COVERED MARKET, OXFORD OX1 3DY
TELEPHONE: 01865 558253
WEBSITE: COLOMBIACOFFEEROASTERS.CO.UK

    COLOMBIAROASTER    COLOMBIACOFFEEROASTERS

One-stop fair trade shopping in central Oxford. Beautiful, unusual gifts and handmade cards to go with them, design-led jewellery, scarves and bags, soap and stationery, toys and textiles, mugs and mobiles, bowls, baskets and LOTS of delicious food. Enabling producer groups around the world to trade their way out of poverty.

WHY WE LOVE IT: PASSIONATE ABOUT FAIR TRADE, THIS HIDDEN GEM OF A SHOP HAS A WHOLE RANGE OF ITEMS FOR HOME AND KITCHEN, AND WE LOVE THAT THEY DO GOOD TOO.

ADDRESS: ST MICHAEL AT THE NORTH GATE, CORNMARKET STREET, OXFORD
             OX1 3EY
TELEPHONE: 01865 722505
WEBSITE: FAIRTRADEATSTMICHAELS.CO.UK

 FTSTMICHAELS    FT_STMICHAELS    FAIRTRADE_AT_STMICHAELS

ISCREAM

We only use traders with the same ethical standards and dedication to perfection to create our light and creamy gelato. We use organic Guernsey milk and cream & machinery from the longest standing Italian gelato engineering company – Carpigiani. We also offer some of the very finest chocolates from around the world.

WHY WE LOVE IT: GRAHAM IS PASSIONATE ABOUT HIS ICE-CREAM'S INGREDIENTS AND IT SHOWS! BUY ICE-CREAM TO EAT NOW AND SOME FANCY CHOCOLATES TO TAKE HOME.

ADDRESS: 113 & 114 COVERED MARKET, OXFORD OX1 3DZ
TELEPHONE: 01865 247084
WEBSITE: ISCREAMOXFORD.CO.UK

 ISCREAMOXFORD    ISCREAMOXFORD    ISCREAMOXFORD

Jemini offers a stunning range of seasonal, fresh flowers, foliage and plants sourced from British and Dutch suppliers. Our stock changes daily and we hand-condition our flowers to ensure that we deliver the freshest flowers for your order which is created by a professionally trained florist who loves what they do.

WHY WE LOVE IT: TALK TO THE FRIENDLY TEAM ABOUT THEIR BEAUTIFUL BOUQUETS FOR SPECIAL OCCASIONS.

ADDRESS: 1/2 THE COVERED MARKET, OXFORD OX1 3DX
TELEPHONE: 01865 242726
WEBSITE: JEMINI.CO.UK

 JEMINIFLOWERSOXFORD

JERICHO COFFEE TRADERS

Conceived in 2012, JCT has evolved from the back of a Vespa tricycle into a roastery and a speciality espresso bar in the heart of Oxford. Run by New Zealander James and his Devonian wife Lizzie, JCT is now also supplying a number of Oxfordshire's best cafés and restaurants with their coffee.

WHY WE LOVE IT: COFFEE OF CHOICE IN MY OFFICE AND AT HOME! FIND A SEAT IN THE CAFE AND ENJOY A CAFFEINE HIT WITH ONE OF THEIR LOCALLY BAKED CAKES.

ADDRESS: ESPRESSO BAR, 105 HIGH STREET, OXFORD OX1 4BW
              ROASTERY, ROGERS HOUSE, OSNEY MEAD, OX2 0ES
TELEPHONE: 07879 400163
WEBSITE: JERICHOCOFFEETRADERS.COM

 JERICHOCOFFEETRADERS    JERICOFFTRADERS    JERICHOCOFFEETRADERS

We are a bright inviting shop selling beautiful clothing and accessories. We sell clothes by Masai, Adini, Cut Loose and Nomads. All these ranges use wonderful fabrics, colours and prints to suit all shapes, styles and prices! We also have the best selection of scarves in Oxford.

WHY WE LOVE IT: SAM HAS A GREAT EYE FOR CURATING COLOURFUL AND STYLISH CLOTHING RANGES. I LOVE HER SEASALT COLLECTION!

ADDRESS: 116-117 THE COVERED MARKET, OXFORD OX1 3DZ
TELEPHONE: 01865 246919
WEBSITE: NEXTTONOTHING.CO

 NEXTTONOTHING    NTN_SHOP

OBJECTS OF USE

Modern day hardware store with a unique collection of everyday household tools, conscientiously sourced from around the globe. Our collection brings together centuries of tradition, passed throughout the hands and minds of generations, whose processes and techniques have culminated in the beautiful tools made using low-impact methods.

WHY WE LOVE IT: A BEAUTIFUL SHOP TO WALK INTO. WE LOVE THEIR UNIFORMLY LAID OUT PRODUCTS AND BEAUTIFUL, INFORMATIVE AND INTERESTING LABELLING.

ADDRESS: 6 LINCOLN HOUSE, MARKET STREET, OXFORD OX1 3EQ
TELEPHONE: 01865 241705
WEBSITE: OBJECTSOFUSE.COM

 OBJECTSOFUSE    OBJECTSOFUSE    OBJECTSOFUSE

The independently owned Old Bank, centrally located on Oxford's famous High, is a breath-taking statement in design. With 42 luxury bedrooms, many have unrivalled views of the surrounding colleges Merton, All Souls, Christ Church and University, and sits proudly opposite the iconic Radcliffe Camera and Bodleian library.

WHY WE LOVE IT: IT REALLY WAS AN OLD BANK BEFORE BEING CONVERTED INTO A MODERN AND STYLISH HOTEL, YET STILL RETAINS MANY OF ITS ORIGINAL FEATURES.

ADDRESS: 92-94 HIGH STREET, OXFORD OX1 4BJ
TELEPHONE: 01865 799599
WEBSITE: OLDBANK-HOTEL.CO.UK

 OLDBANKHOTEL    OLDBANKHOTEL    OLDBANKHOTEL

OLIVIA MAY

Olivia May womenswear boutique prides itself on providing the unconventional for the independent woman who knows her own mind and doesn't follow the high street fashion. The shop to find that one off piece you can't live without or a show stopping outfit for any occasion.

WHY WE LOVE IT: IT REALLY SHINES THROUGH HERE THAT THE LADIES HERE KNOW THE BRANDS THEY STOCK AND LOVE WHAT THEY DO!

ADDRESS: 31 LITTLE CLARENDON STREET, OXFORD OX1 2HU
TELEPHONE: 01865 515336
WEBSITE: OLIVIAMAY.ORG

 OLIVIAMAYCLOTHING    OLIVIAMAYLTD    OLIVIAMAYOXFORD

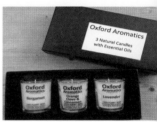

Full of fabulously aromatic products from essential oils to natural candles, lip balms to reed diffusers. We source our products mainly from small UK suppliers who, like us, care about providing quality products at affordable prices. Come in and smell for yourself!

WHY WE LOVE IT: FIND A WHOLE HOST OF GORGEOUS CANDLES AND TOILETRIES MADE IN THE UK AND AN EXTENSIVE COLLECTION OF ESSENTIAL OILS.

ADDRESS: 44 - 45 THE COVERED MARKET, OXFORD OX1 3DX
TELEPHONE: 01865 250797
WEBSITE: OXFORDAROMATICS.CO.UK

 OXFORDAROMATICS

 OXFORDAROMATICS

PAYNE & SON

Eighth generation family business, established 1790. Payne & Son specialises in 20th century and contemporary silver, as well as modern and traditional jewellery in gold, platinum and silver. We have an extensive ring collection featuring rare coloured stones and bespoke wedding rings, and are a major stockist of Georg Jensen.

WHY WE LOVE IT: THE HIGH ST WOULD NOT BE THE SAME WITHOUT THIS FAMILY OWNED GEM. TALK TO THE FRIENDLY STAFF TO FIND YOUR PERFECT ENGAGEMENT RING.

ADDRESS: 131 HIGH STREET, OXFORD OX1 4DH
TELEPHONE: 01865 243787
WEBSITE: PAYNEANDSON.CO.UK

 PAYNEANDSONOXFORD    PAYNESONOXFORD    PAYNEANDSON

Pint Shop is all about craft products delivered in a relaxing surrounding. Our bar lists 21 draft beers, 100 gins and 100 whiskies alongside our famous Scotch Eggs. In our Dining Room, we cook simple, seasonal British food over local charcoal and wood.

WHY WE LOVE IT: HUGE COLLECTION OF CRAFT BEERS, GINS AND WHISKIES. BAR SNACKS ARE NEXT LEVEL AND THE RESTAURANT DOWNSTAIRS HAS A GREAT MENU AT VERY GOOD VALUE. ONE OF OUR FAVOURITES.

ADDRESS: 27-29 GEORGE STREET, OXFORD OX1 2AU
TELEPHONE: 01865 251194
WEBSITE: PINTSHOP.CO.UK

 MEATBREADBEER   PINTSHOP    PINT_SHOP

PODAROK

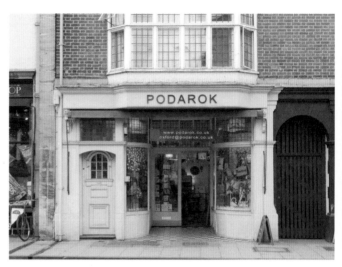

Podarok is a real true Indie, calling itself 'Oxford's Boutique Emporium.' They are jam-packed full of lovelies and pretties, from unique quirky handbags and manbags, to British-designed jewellery and handmade lampshades. The one-stop-gift-shop!

WHY WE LOVE IT: A GREAT GIFT SHOP AT THE END OF THE HIGH STREET WITH A BEAUTIFUL RANGE OF ITEMS. THEY'VE ALSO GOT A FRIENDLY TEAM WHO LOVE HAVING A NATTER!

ADDRESS: 55 HIGH ST, OXFORD OX1 4AS
TELEPHONE: 01685 236680
WEBSITE: PODAROK.CO.UK

 PODAROKSHOP    PODAROKSHOP    PODAROKSHOP

On Oxford's bustling High Street, peering out onto St Mary's Church and the iconic Radcliffe Camera, Quod Restaurant forms the lively hub of the Old Bank Hotel. Regulars and visitors alike flock to Quod for its European classics menu with an emphasis on British produce, some of which is sourced from Jeremy Mogford's own Rofford Farm.

WHY WE LOVE IT: BRASSERIE WTH A STUNNING ONYX BAR IN THE CENTRE OF A LARGE OPEN SPACE. SEASONAL MENU AND A GREAT LUNCH OFFER.

ADDRESS: 92-94 HIGH STREET, OXFORD OX1 4BJ
TELEPHONE: 01865 202505
WEBSITE: QUOD.CO.UK

 QUODRESTAURANT    QUODRESTAURANT    QUODRESTAURANT

RAINBOW AND SPOON BOUTIQUE

Located in a pretty flower filled courtyard, Rainbow and Spoon was established in 1982 and is the place to go for stylish and individual clothing, gifts, and fabulous accessories. We pride ourselves on our friendly service, Fairtrade credentials and affordability. Please pay us a visit - you won't be disappointed!

WHY WE LOVE IT: AMANDA'S SHOP IS A COLOURFUL EMPORIUM OF FASHION AND ACCESSORIES. IF YOU NEED A COLOURFUL PICK-ME-UP, MAKE A BEELINE TO RAINBOW AND SPOON!

ADDRESS: 22 PARK END STREET, FRIDESWIDE SQUARE, OXFORD OX1 1HU
TELEPHONE: 01865 723492
WEBSITE: RAINBOWANDSPOON.CO.UK

RAINBOWANDSPOONBOUTIQUE   RAINBOWANDSPOON   RAINBOWANDSPOON

Sanders of Oxford are one of the largest antique print and map sellers in Britain and have long been a landmark on Oxford's High Street. Our varied stock, dating from 16th to 20th century, covers all subjects, from stunning regional and world maps to Japanese woodblock prints.

WHY WE LOVE IT: A HIGH STREET INSTITUTION AND ONE STOP SHOP FOR PRINTS FROM MODERN TO ANTIQUE. YOU CAN LOSE YOURSELF IN THIS PRINT GOLDMINE!

ADDRESS: 104 HIGH STREET, OXFORD OX1 4BW
TELEPHONE: 01865 242590
WEBSITE: SANDERSOFOXFORD.COM

 SANDERSOFOXFORD    SANDERSOFOXFORD    SANDERS_OF_OXFORD

SHOP AT THE OLD FIRE STATION

A cheeky and colourful lifestyle shop with jewellery, homewares, textiles, prints and stationery. All our goods are from UK indie designer-makers and most are handmade. As part of Arts at OFS, money from your purchases goes into our charity work with Crisis, providing training and volunteering opportunities for homeless people.

WHY WE LOVE IT: A GREAT RANGE OF HOMEWARE, JEWELLERY, PRINTS AND MORE THAT FUNDS PROJECTS AT THE ARTS CENTRE AND CRISIS SKYLIGHT. FEEL GOOD SHOPPING!

ADDRESS: GLOUCESTER GREEN, OXFORD OX1 2AQ
TELEPHONE: 01865 263987
WEBSITE: OLDFIRESTATION.ORG.UK/SHOP

 ARTSATTHEOLDFIRESTATION   SHOPATOFS    SHOPATOFS

We are a speciality coffee shop right in the heart of Oxford City Centre. Stunning coffee in a beautiful shop with a fabulous selection of indie magazines & books. Also serving amazing loose leaf teas, bespoke hot chocolates, and incredible cakes by Barefoot Oxford.

WHY WE LOVE IT: THE STAFF HERE REALLY KNOW THEIR COFFEES, WITH A REGULAR GUEST BEAN. COOL AND FUNKY, THIS IS A GREAT PLACE FOR YOUR CAFFEINE FIX. FAB BAKES TOO!

ADDRESS: 12-16 ST. MICHAELS STREET, OXFORD OX1 2DU
TELEPHONE: 01865 425750
WEBSITE: SOCIETY-CAFE.COM

 SOCIETYCAFE    SOCIETYCAFE    SOCIETYCAFE

SOFI DE FRANCE

Very popular cafe that offers a great selection of panini, ciabatta, baguettes, sandwiches, coffee and pastries.

WHY WE LOVE IT: A FRIENDLY FAMILY RUN CAFE IN THE HEART OF THE COVERED MARKET, TRY THEIR DELICIOUS BAKLAVA!

ADDRESS: 33-36 THE COVERED MARKET, OXFORD OX1 3DX
TELEPHONE: 01865 249858
WEBSITE: CAFEDUMARCHE-OXFORD.COM

 SOFIDEFRANCE    SOFI_DE_FRANCE

Slap bang in the city centre, yet also slightly hidden, St Ebbe's Kitchen is the lunch spot you long to stumble across. Fiona and Lorraine have created a friendly, buzzy atmosphere and offer a short, considered, seasonal menu bursting with flavours – including salads the like of which you will not find elsewhere!

WHY WE LOVE IT: WHETHER MODERN ART IS YOUR THING OR NOT, MAKE A POINT OF GOING HERE FOR LUNCH. A SMALL AND MAINLY PLANT BASED MENU WITH A HUGE RANGE OF FLAVOURS IN THEIR SOUPS, TOASTIES, QUICHE, SALADS & CAKES.

ADDRESS: 30 PEMBROKE STREET, OXFORD OX11BP
TELEPHONE: 01865 201491
WEBSITE: STEBBESKITCHEN.CO.UK

 STEBBESKITCHEN    STEBBESKITCHEN

THE COVERED MARKET

Located in the centre of Oxford, the Covered Market welcomes visitors with an array of colours and aromas. We are proud that the majority of our businesses are independent, some going back generations. With over 40 traders selling food, gifts, shoes, fashion, flowers and jewellery, it is the unique 'one stop shop'.

WHY WE LOVE IT: A JEWEL IN OXFORD'S CROWN, THE COVERED MARKET ABSOLUTELY DESERVES ITS HISTORICAL SIGNIFICANCE. GO FOR MEAT, VEG, LUNCH, MILKSHAKES, COOKIES, ICE-CREAM, FLOWERS AND SO MUCH MORE!

ADDRESS: MARKET STREET, OXFORD OX1 3DZ
TELEPHONE:
WEBSITE: OXFORD-COVEREDMARKET.CO.UK

 THECOVEREDMARKETOXFORD  COVEREDMARKETOX  THECOVEREDMARKETOXFORD

A quirky cafe with bikes hanging off the ceiling, wooden floors and beams, large bright windows and a buzzy, cozy atmosphere. We serve breakfast, lunch and dinner, all made with love and carefully sourced ingredients from local independent suppliers. There's always exciting vegan, vegetarian and gluten free dishes on the menu.

WHY WE LOVE IT: A FOODIE GEM IN THE HEART OF OXFORD! SETTLE DOWN TO A HEARTY BRUNCH OR DELICIOUS EVENING MEAL.

ADDRESS: 28-32 ST MICHAEL'S STREET, OXFORD OX1 2EB
TELEPHONE: 01865 251315
WEBSITE: HANDLEBAROXFORD.CO.UK

 HANDLEBAROXFORD    HANDLEBAROXFORD    HANDLEBAROXFORD

THE HAT BOX

We are passionate about hats. We stock a huge range of ladies hats and fascinators in over 100 colours. We also stock men's hats and caps including top hats and bowlers. Do come and visit us.

WHY WE LOVE IT: STOP BY FOR MEN'S AND WOMENS HATS OF ALL SHAPES AND SIZES, OR CHAT TO GILLIAN ABOUT CUSTOMISED HATS FOR SPECIAL OCCASIONS.

ADDRESS: AVENUE 3, THE COVERED MARKET, OXFORD OX1 3DY
TELEPHONE: 01865 200844
WEBSITE: THEHATBOXOXFORD.COM

 HATBOXOXFORD    THEHATBOXOXFORD    THEHATBOX_OXFORD

The Leather Shop has been in Oxford since 1972. We have an eclectic range of leather goods from briefcases to leather animals. We take leather repairs in bags and are always happy to answer any questions. If you love the smell of leather, do come in and have a sniff!

WHY WE LOVE IT: IF YOU LOVE THE SMELL OF LEATHER THEN YOU'LL LOVE THIS SHOP! A VAST RANGE OF LEATHER PRODUCTS FROM SMALL PURSES TO LARGE BAGS.

ADDRESS: 4 TURL STREET, OXFORD OX1 3DQ
TELEPHONE: 01865 790309
WEBSITE: PLAINLEATHER.CO.UK

 THELEATHERSHOPOXFORD

 THELEATHERSHOPOXFORD

THE MISSING BEAN

The Missing Bean has been serving top notch coffee since they opened in 2009. Always busy and bustling with lots of homemade cakes, many vegan or gluten free. They also roast their own beans, over at their Roastery Cafe in East Oxford.

WHY WE LOVE IT: ALWAYS BUSY BUT WORTH HANGING AROUND TO GET A SEAT! THESE GUYS REALLY KNOW THEIR BEANS.

ADDRESS: 14 TURL STREET, OXFORD OX1 3DQ
TELEPHONE: 01865 794886
WEBSITE: THEMISSINGBEAN.CO.UK

 THEMISSINGBEAN
 THEMISSINGBEAN
 THEMISSINGBEAN

Fresh cold pressed juices and smoothies, great coffee and delicious healthy cakes. Our menu reflects seasonal and locally sourced produce.

WHY WE LOVE IT: GREAT SELECTION OF FRUIT SMOOTHIES, DIFFERENT TO THE USUAL BLENDS. THERE'S ALWAYS A RANGE OF CAKES & BAKES ON OFFER, SOME OBVIOUSLY HEALTHY AND SOME YOU WOULDN'T EVEN KNOW ARE!

ADDRESS: 16 THE COVERED MARKET, OXFORD OX1 3DZ
TELEPHONE:
WEBSITE: THENATURALBUZZ.UK

 THENATURALBUZZ
 THENATURALBUZZUK

THENA

Thena is an independent women's boutique based in Oxford's Covered Market. Our shop is a treasure trove of gorgeous handmade clothes and accessories. We specialise in beautiful dresses ideal for balls, proms, weddings and parties!

WHY WE LOVE IT: VISIT LOVELY RATANA AND GET YOUR OUTFIT SORTED FOR YOUR UNI BALL OR SPECIAL OCCASION.

ADDRESS: 101-102 AVENUE 3, THE COVERED MARKET, OXFORD OX1 3DY
TELEPHONE: 01865 251153
WEBSITE:

 THENAOXFORD

We are a busy, city centre restaurant-with-rooms and a registered social enterprise. We source food that is local, seasonal, and fresh, and also support local artists and artisans. We are a member of the Sustainable Restaurant Association and have been featured in The Good Food Guide and Sawdays Special Places.

WHY WE LOVE IT: ANNA & I ARE BIG FANS OF TSK WHO HAVE BEEN VERY SUPPORTIVE OF US AT INDIE OXFORD, PLUS THEIR FOOD IS DELICIOUS AND SERVED BY A SUPER FRIENDLY TEAM!

ADDRESS: 16-17 TURL STREET, OXFORD OX1 3DH
TELEPHONE: 01865 246171
WEBSITE: TURLSTREETKITCHEN.CO.UK

 TURLSTREETKITCHEN    TURLSTKITCHEN    TURLSTREETKITCHEN

43

~~GOOD THINGS COME TO
THOSE WHO WAIT~~

GOOD THINGS COME TO
THOSE WHO WORK THEIR
ASSES OFF AND
NEVER GIVE UP

OX2

NORTH & WEST OXFORD

Encompassing Jericho, Botley and Summertown to the North and West of the city, you'll find a whole host of wonderful indies in OX2. From artisan bakeries and warehouse bars to exceptional florists and independent galleries, this area has a lot to offer the discerning independent shopper. Explore little and often or plan your route from one excellent eatery to the next combined with a stroll through the famous Port Meadow.

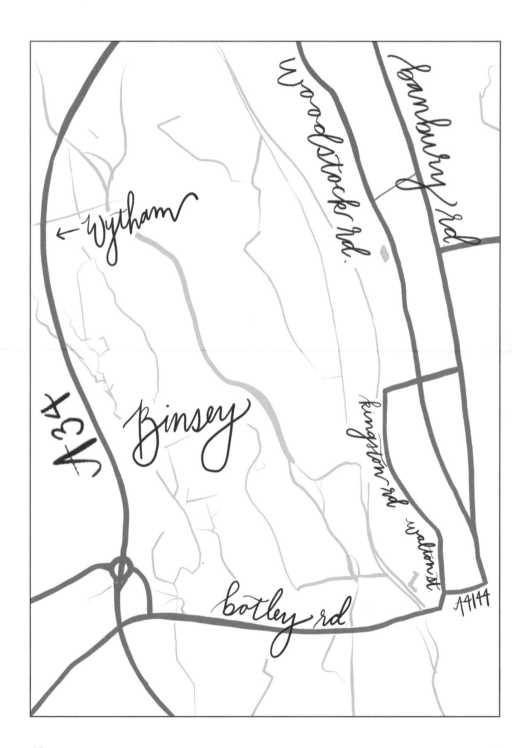

A friendly neighbourhood shop that sources the best produce for your table. Whether it's local organic fruit and veg, artisan sourdough bread or British farmhouse cheese, you'll always find the best, because good cooking starts with good ingredients.

WHY WE LOVE IT: A GORGEOUS NEIGHBOURHOOD GROCERS WITH DELICIOUS LOCAL PRODUCE. TALK TO PETE & JOJO ABOUT RECIPE INSPIRATION!

ADDRESS: 2 NORTH PARADE AVENUE, OXFORD OX2 6LX
TELEPHONE: 01865 552311
WEBSITE: 2NORTHPARADE.COM

    2NORTHPARADE    2NORTHPARADE

BAREFOOT KITCHEN

Located in the heart of Jericho, Barefoot is the place to go for gorgeous cakes, quirky flavours and stunning decorations. Enjoy one of our renowned brownies and a coffee or take a slice home for tea. We cater for dietary restrictions too because cake is for everyone!

WHY WE LOVE IT: THE MOST BEAUTIFUL CAKES - COURGETTE AND LIME IS A FAVOURITE, AS IS THE CHOCOLATE STOUT CAKE. AND THE BROWNIES. IN FACT, THEY'RE ALL FABULOUS!

ADDRESS: 74A WALTON STREET, OXFORD OX2 6EA
TELEPHONE: 07814 495001
WEBSITE: BAREFOOTOXFORD.CO.UK

 BAREFOOTOXFORD

 BAREFOOTOXFORD

Cannelle Beauty offers clients essential beauty and advanced aesthetic treatments in a relaxing, pristine environment. Treatments include Decleor facials, massage, body treatments, ESSIE & Biosculpture manicures, pedicures and waxing as well as more advanced solutions.

WHY WE LOVE IT: EXPERTLY EXECUTED TREATMENTS IN A POLISHED SETTING, WITH FRIENDLY STAFF AND AN EYE ON THE LATEST BEAUTY TREATMENTS.

ADDRESS: 1A OAKTHORPE ROAD, SUMMERTOWN, OXFORD OX2 7BD
TELEPHONE: 01865 511960
WEBSITE: CANNELLEBEAUTY.CO.UK

 CANNELLEBEAUTY    CANNELLEBEAUTE    CANNELLEBEAUTE

DAISIES FLOWER SHOP

Based in Jericho since 1987, we're delighted to do flowers for the loveliest people in Oxford and around the world. Come and talk to us about flowers for the happy times - the freshest bouquets, gorgeous weddings, stylish business events - and for the sad times. Never dull, always beautiful!

WHY WE LOVE IT: THE TEAM HERE ARE WONDERFULLY HELPFUL AND KNOW THEIR FLOWERS FROM THEIR FOLIAGE! THEY'RE ALWAYS HAPPY TO HELP YOU CREATE SOMETHING BEAUTIFUL.

ADDRESS: 106 WALTON STREET, OXFORD OX2 6AJ
TELEPHONE: 01865 554882
WEBSITE: DAISIES-FLOWER-SHOP.CO.UK

 DAISIESFLOWERSHOP

 DAISIESOXFORD

Exclusive Roots is a unique store specialising in contemporary handcrafted products from Africa. Our Woodstock Road store is bursting with jewellery from Kenya, ceramics from South Africa, scarves from Ethiopia, and bags from Malawi. The shop also houses a large range of beautiful baskets made by skilled crafters in Ghana, Rwanda, and Senegal.

WHY WE LOVE IT: WE LOVE THAT AS A CHARITY, THE MONEY YOU SPEND ON THE GORGEOUS ITEMS IN THE STORE GOES DIRECTLY BACK TO THE SUPPLIERS THAT EXCLUSIVE ROOTS SUPPORTS.

ADDRESS: 8 WOODSTOCK ROAD, OXFORD OX2 6HT
TELEPHONE: 01865 511992
WEBSITE: EXCLUSIVEROOTS.COM

 EXCLUSIVEROOTSOXFORD    EXCLUSIVEROOTS

FABULOUS FLOWERS

Fabulous Flowers is a premier florist with shops in Oxford and Abingdon. Fabulous Flowers provides flowers for weddings, events, gifts and a corporate bespoke flower service.

WHY WE LOVE IT: FLOWERS GALORE AND A DREAM FOR ANY INSTAGRAMMER. THE FABULOUS TEAM HERE KNOW THEIR FLOWERS AND CREATE STUNNING DISPLAYS!

ADDRESS: 63 BANBURY ROAD, OXFORD OX2 6PG
TELEPHONE: 01865 511811
WEBSITE: FABULOUSFLOWERS.BIZ

 FABFLOWERSOXFORD    FABFLOWERS    FABULOUSFLOWERS

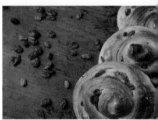

Independently owned and situated in the upmarket Summertown area of Oxford, Gatineau offers the finest artisan produce in the French/European patisserie and boulangerie tradition: premium cakes, chocolates, pastries, savouries and breads – all made in house with the highest quality ingredients, creative flair and taste combinations.

WHY WE LOVE IT: OOH LA LA! MAKE LIKE YOU'RE IN PARIS AND ENJOY THE SUMPTUOUS PATISSERIE ON OFFER.

ADDRESS: 209 BANBURY ROAD, SUMMERTOWN, OXFORD OX2 7HQ
TELEPHONE: 01865 311779
WEBSITE: GATINEAU.UK.COM

 GATINEAU.LTD    GATINEAULTD    GATINEAU.LTD

GEE'S RESTAURANT & BAR

Gee's Restaurant offers locals and visitors a uniquely rustic, Mediterranean dining experience set in an iconic Victorian Glasshouse. Enjoy a house cocktail at the marble topped bar, dine in the light-filled conservatory amidst olive trees and plants, and choose from a daily evolving seasonal menu.

WHY WE LOVE IT: WONDERFUL VENUE AND FAB FOOD. PERFECT FOR A SPECIAL OCCASION.

ADDRESS: 61 BANBURY ROAD, OXFORD OX2 6PE
TELEPHONE: 01865 553540
WEBSITE: GEES-RESTAURANT.CO.UK

 GEESRESTAURANT    GEESRESTAURANT    GEESRESTAURANT

A curated selection of British and Irish farmhouse cheeses and dairy products together with a small range of high quality accompaniments.

WHY WE LOVE IT: WE LOVE THAT THEY REGULARLY INVITE SUPPLIERS IN SO YOU CAN EAT CHEESE WHILE CHATTING TO THE PRODUCERS ABOUT THEIR ANIMALS AND PROCESSES.

ADDRESS: 25 LITTLE CLARENDON STREET, OXFORD OX1 2HU
TELEPHONE: 01865 516000
WEBSITE: JERICHOCHEESE.CO.UK

 JERICHOCHEESE
 JERICHOCHEESECO
 JERICHOCHEESE

MAMMA MIA PIZZERIA

An Oxford institution for over 35 years, combining traditional, authentic recipes, fabulous imported Italian ingredients and a relaxed, family friendly atmosphere to bring a little bit of Naples to Oxford. So good we were even named the best Independent Pizza Restaurant in the UK! Also find us in Jericho.

WHY WE LOVE IT: LOCATED IN BOTH SUMMERTOWN AND JERICHO, MAMMA MIA REALLY IS AN INSTITUTION WITH ITS AUTHENTIC ITALIAN DISHES.

ADDRESS: 8 SOUTH PARADE, OXFORD OX2 7JL
TELEPHONE: 01865 514141
WEBSITE: MAMMAMIAPIZZERIA.CO.UK

 MAMMAMIAOXFORD    MAMMAMIAOXFORD    MAMMAMIAOXFORD

At Modern Baker, bread is not unhealthy and baking is not an indulgence. Focusing on provenance, nutrition and taste, our food excites your taste buds and delights your body. Come in and relax with a turmeric latte and some raw millionaire's shortbread or just pick up your daily loaf.

WHY WE LOVE IT: WANT TO EAT DELICIOUS CAKES AND BREAD AND NOT FEEL GUILTY? THIS IS THE PLACE TO GO. WE LOVE THEIR HEALTHY TAKE ON BAKERY.

ADDRESS: 214A BANBURY ROAD, SUMMERTOWN, OXFORD OX2 7BY
TELEPHONE: 01865 554679
WEBSITE: MODERNBAKER.COM

 MODERNBAKERNATURALFOOD    MODERN_BAKER    MODERNBAKER

OLD PARSONAGE HOTEL

Our 17th century hotel combines original charm and character with all the luxury, amenities and technology available to an independently owned 5* hotel. Best known by locals and visitors alike for its eclectic country house charm, chic modern interiors and striking 20th century portraits, the Old Parsonage is a luxury home-from-home.

WHY WE LOVE IT: QUIRKY, ECLECTIC AND JUST WONDERFULLY CHARMING. STEP INSIDE THIS BEAUTIFUL BUILDING AND YOU'LL INSTANTLY FEEL AT HOME IN THE OLD PARSONAGE'S COSY ROOMS.

ADDRESS: 1-3 BANBURY ROAD, OXFORD OX2 6NN
TELEPHONE: 01865 310210
WEBSITE: OLDPARSONAGE-HOTEL.CO.UK

 OLDPARSONAGEHOTEL    OLDPARSONAGEOX    OLDPARSONAGEHOTEL

Oxford Yarn Store provides knitters and crocheters with the most sumptuous yarns from around the globe, as well as related patterns, books and accessories. It also has a programme of workshops and Knit Clubs that make it a social hub for those who take pleasure in hand crafts.

WHY WE LOVE IT: HEAVEN FOR KNITTERS! WE LOVE THE RANGE OF WOOLS AND THE FACT THEY RUN WORKSHOPS FOR BEGINNERS AND KNITTING PROS!

ADDRESS: 3 NORTH PARADE AVENUE, OXFORD OX2 6LX
TELEPHONE: 01865 604112
WEBSITE: OXFORDYARNSTORE.CO.UK

 OXFORDYARNSTORE

PARSONAGE GRILL

Parsonage Grill's state of the art kitchen uses the best local produce to create classic, simple yet innovative British dishes. Open every day of the year, enjoy breakfast, lunch, dinner and our famous afternoon teas in the company of Oxford's academic and literary luminaries.

WHY WE LOVE IT: SERIOUSLY GOOD FOOD, ONE OF THE TOP PLACES IN TOWN FOR AFTERNOON TEA AND WORTH RETURNING FOR DINNER IF YOU CAN MANAGE IT!

ADDRESS: 1-3 BANBURY ROAD, OXFORD OX2 6NN
TELEPHONE: 01865 292305
WEBSITE: PARSONAGEGRILL.CO.UK

 PARSONAGEGRILL    PARSONAGEGRILL    PARSONAGEGRILL

All-day neighbourhood restaurant and bar serving a range of great steaks and burgers in a stylish, relaxed setting. Weekend Brunch is a speciality, or enjoy a cocktail on the terrace when the sun shines. Private dining room above the restaurant is the perfect venue for celebrations, gatherings and meetings.

WHY WE LOVE IT: WE'LL HAPPILY TRAVEL ACROSS TOWN FOR A PORTABELLO BRUNCH! MODERN, LIGHT BISTRO WITH A CONTEMPORARY MENU.

ADDRESS: 7 SOUTH PARADE, SUMMERTOWN, OXFORD OX2 7JL
TELEPHONE: 01865 559653
WEBSITE: PORTABELLORESTAURANT.CO.UK

 PORTABELLOXFORD    PORTABELLOXFORD    PORTABELLOXFORD

SARAH WISEMAN GALLERY

We are Oxford's largest independent gallery, specialising in contemporary painting. Director Sarah Wiseman has sought out a group of artists with an eye to individuality and technical accomplishment. The Gallery is a leading destination for exceptional and inspiring contemporary art by established and emerging creative talent.

WHY WE LOVE IT: SARAH AND HER TEAM ARE EXPERTS IN CURATING CONTEMPORARY ART AND ARE REAL ADVOCATES OF THE INDEPENDENT SCENE IN OXFORD.

ADDRESS: 40-41 SOUTH PARADE, SUMMERTOWN, OXFORD OX2 7JL
TELEPHONE: 01865 515123
WEBSITE: WISEGAL.COM

 SARAHWISEMANGALLERY    SARAH_WISEGAL    SARAH_WISEMAN_GALLERY

Tap Social Movement is an Oxford-based craft brewery specialising in (vegan-friendly!) real ale, with sours comprising half our core range. We work with people serving prison sentences, offering training in brewing and business start-up, and providing one-on-one support in securing permanent employment to assist in effective rehabilitation.

WHY WE LOVE IT: POSSIBLY THE MOST HIPSTER PLACE IN OXFORD BUT YOU CAN FORGIVE THAT BECAUSE THEY HAVE A GREAT SELECTION OF ALES. ENJOY A BEER KNOWING THAT YOU ARE SUPPORTING A COMMUNITY VENTURE.

ADDRESS: 27 CURTIS INDUSTRIAL ESTATE, NORTH HINKSEY LANE, OXFORD
             OX2 0LX
TELEPHONE: 01865 236330
WEBSITE: TAPSOCIALMOVEMENT.COM

 TAPSOCIALMOVEMENT    TAPSOCIALBREW    TAPSOCIALMOVEMENT

THE JERICHO CAFE

The Jericho Cafe is a real 'local' café with a bustling, buzzy vibe. We have an extensive brunch menu, offer a range of vegan and gluten free options and will accommodate all dietary requirements wherever possible. The perfect place to chill out and catch up with old friends.

WHY WE LOVE IT: A BOHEMIAN CAFE IN THE HEART OF JERICHO, SERVING UNCOMPLICATED FOOD BUT WITH HIGH QUALITY INGREDIENTS THAT MAKE ALL THE DIFFERENCE. A BREAKFAST FAVOURITE.

ADDRESS: 112 WALTON STREET, OXFORD OX2 6AJ
TELEPHONE: 01865 310840
WEBSITE: THEJERICHOCAFE.CO.UK

  JERICHO_CAFE  THEJERICHOCAFE

One of Oxford's oldest pubs, our beautiful garden and thatched 17th Century building provide a refuge for anyone who loves great food and drink – be it thirsty students, hungry walkers, exploring families, muddy dogs, adventurous visitors or wedding parties.

WHY WE LOVE IT: HAVE A WALK THROUGH PORT MEADOW TO THE PERCH, HAVE A PINT AND PERUSE THEIR BRITISH FARMHOUSE SEASONAL MENU WITH SOMETHING FOR EVERYONE, INCLUDING VEGAN OPTIONS.

ADDRESS: BINSEY LANE, OXFORD OX2 ONG
TELEPHONE: 01865 728891
WEBSITE: THE-PERCH.CO.UK

 THEPERCHOXFORD
 THEPERCHOXFORD
 THEPERCHOXFORD

THE WHITE HART

Our 16th century country village pub and dining just 2 miles from Oxford city centre has roaring log fires in winter, and a sunny secluded courtyard in summer. All our food is locally sourced and we love everything roasted, smoked, pickled and cured. We also have a beautiful Georgian stable room also available for special occasions.

WHY WE LOVE IT: WE LOVE THIS PLACE! IN SUMMER, SIT ON THE PATIO AND ENJOY THE FRAGRANT HERB GARDEN. IN WINTER, SIT BY THE FIRE AND SUP ONE OF THEIR ALES. EATING HERE IS AN ABSOLUTE HIGHLIGHT ALL YEAR ROUND.

ADDRESS: WYTHAM, OXFORD OX2 8QA
TELEPHONE: 01865 244372
WEBSITE: WHITEHARTWYTHAM.COM

 WHITEHARTWYTHAM    WHITEHARTOFWYTHAM    WHITEHARTOFWYTHAM

Family run, fast-paced restaurant in Jericho. The underlying influence of our food is unmistakeably Oriental, from authentic Malaysian and Singaporean to spicy Szechuan, Cantonese stir-fries and Shanghai braises. The Times' Giles Coren called us "Possibly the best authentic Chinese/Malaysian in the country".

WHY WE LOVE IT: ONE OF OUR FAVOURITES, INTENSE FLAVOURS AND TEXTURES IN A CONSTANTLY BUSY RESTAURANT. WE LOVE THE CEREAL PRAWNS!

ADDRESS: 82 WALTON STREET, OXFORD OX2 6EA
TELEPHONE: 01865 558888
WEBSITE: ZHENGOXFORD.CO.UK

 ZHENGOXFORD

THEY CALL US DREAMERS, BUT WE'RE THE ONES WHO DON'T SLEEP

A real gem of a restaurant serving brunch, lunch and dinner. Arguably one of the best breakfasts in Oxford, served all day, alongside our seasonal menus and outstanding sourdough pizzas. Recently mentioned as one of The Telegraph's Top 30 places to brunch.

WHY WE LOVE IT: MORE CASUAL THAN THE OTHER JACOBS, THIS IS A VERY POPULAR VENUE IN HEADINGTON. STOP FOR COFFEE AND CAKE, BRUNCH OR DINNER, ALL WITH HIGH QUALITY, LOCALLY SOURCED INGREDIENTS.

ADDRESS: 15 OLD HIGH STREET, HEADINGTON, OXFORD OX3 9HP
TELEPHONE: 01865 766990
WEBSITE: JACOBSANDFIELD.COM

 JACOBSANDFIELD    JACOBSANDFIELD

JACOBS BRASSERIE

Jacobs brasserie brings the familiar all day dining atmosphere from the House of Jacob team with superb, locally sourced ingredients and a relaxed yet sophisticated dining experience. Open seven days a week, our bustling restaurant is the perfect space for a casual lunch, after work drink, or an intimate dinner.

WHY WE LOVE IT: A BRASSERIE WITH SOME TRADITIONAL FRENCH DISHES AND SOME SLIGHTLY DIFFERENT OPTIONS. GOOD STEAK AND GREAT COCKTAILS!

ADDRESS: 3 OSLER ROAD, HEADINGTON, OXFORD OX3 7RA
TELEPHONE: 01865 764486
WEBSITE: JACOBSBRASSERIE.COM

 JACOBSBRASSERIE    JACOBSBRASSERIE

We are an individual unique boutique hair salon located in Headington. We pride ourselves on our attention to detail and our ability to create an array of beautiful colours and haircuts at affordable prices. We are also very proud to have recently been awarded best hair salon in Oxford. Parking available.

WHY WE LOVE IT: ROSIE AND I HAVE BEEN COMING HERE SINCE LOUISE AND HER SISTER OPENED THE SALON. GREAT SERVICE AND CUTS EVERY TIME AND NOT AFRAID TO TRY SOMETHING DIFFERENT!

ADDRESS: 6 CINNAMINTA ROAD, HEADINGTON, OXFORD OX3 7JB
TELEPHONE: 01865 236390
WEBSITE: KENNYSHAIRBOUTIQUE.COM

 KENNYSHAIRBOUTIQUE    KENNYSHAIRBOUTIQUE

BIG THINGS OFTEN SMALL HAVE BEGINNINGS

OX4

EAST OXFORD

Head over Magdalen Bridge to the East of the city and you'll find St Clements, Cowley Road and Iffley Road. Known for its diversity and mix of town and gown, this combination of cultures results in a restaurant scene that's a gold mine for food lovers! Try Italian, Moroccan, fresh seafood or amazing steak all within the same area. But the indies don't stop there, OX4 is awash with specialist and lifestyle shops, Oxford's only independent cinema, and is home to the Cowley Road Carnival that takes place every July.

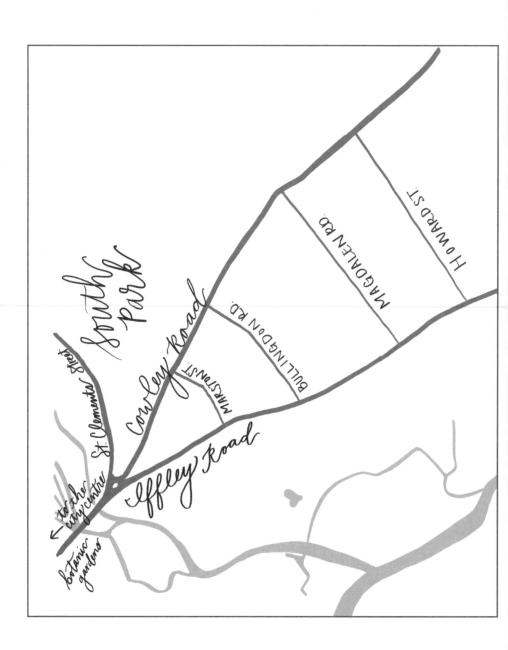

ATOMIC BURGER

The original Atomic that started it all! Relive your childhood with our collection of toys, pictures and memorabilia whilst feasting on our amazing burgers; beef, chicken or veggie with a whole range of toppings, loaded fries and thick milkshakes. GF available and our veggie burger was voted best in Oxford by Bitten!

WHY WE LOVE IT: QUITE POSSIBLY THE BEST BURGERS IN OXFORD AND GREAT VEGGIE BURGERS TOO! RELIVE YOUR CHILDHOOD WITH ALL THEIR FAB DECOR.

ADDRESS: 92 COWLEY ROAD, OXFORD OX4 1JE
TELEPHONE: 01865 790855
WEBSITE: ATOMICBURGER.CO.UK

 ATOMICBURGER
 ATOMICBURGERS
 ATOMICBURGER

ATOMIC PIZZA

Giving pizzas the Atomic treatment as well as serving the burgers that their sister restaurant is famous for, they offer a wide range of loaded pizzas. From pulled pork to Cajun onion rings, you'll find them all on an Atomic Pizza!

WHY WE LOVE IT: SIBLING OF ATOMIC BURGER DOWN THE ROAD BUT WITH THE OPTION TO HAVE THOSE BURGER TOPPINGS ON A PIZZA BASE!

ADDRESS: 247 COWLEY ROAD, OXFORD OX4 1XG
TELEPHONE: 01865 248200
WEBSITE: ATOMICPIZZAS.CO.UK

 ATOMICPIZZA

 ATOMICPIZZAS

 ATOMICPIZZAS

BICYCLE BLOOMS

Bicycle Blooms, a new artisan flower shop in East Oxford creating bespoke bouquets for all occasions. Emphasis on seasonal flowers, seed heads, berries and foliage that reflect the year, and surrounded by potted plants and containers to go. Delivers in and around Oxford. Workshops held throughout the year, so keep an eye on the website.

WHY WE LOVE IT: A NEW FAVOURITE FOR US! GORGEOUS BLOOMS AND BRILLIANT CUSTOMER SERVICE.

ADDRESS: 138 MAGDALEN ROAD, OXFORD OX4 1RJ
TELEPHONE: 01865 200281
WEBSITE: BICYCLEBLOOMS.COM

 BICYCLEBLOOMS    BICYCLEBLOOMSOXFORD

BROWNS

This modern update of the British Guest House is the perfect base when visiting Oxford. Our 11 unique bedrooms come with a fresh mix of antique and retro furniture, each fitted out with a mixture of stylish design pieces, locally roasted coffee, handmade artisan soaps and modern art prints.

WHY WE LOVE IT: A LOVELY GUEST HOUSE IN THE HEART OF EAST OXFORD WITH GREAT LINKS TO TOWN. THE ROOMS ARE GORGEOUS AND HAVE BEEN FRESHLY DECORATED IN A CONTEMPORARY STYLE WITH VINTAGE ACCENT PIECES.

ADDRESS: 281 IFFLEY ROAD, OXFORD OX4 4AQ
TELEPHONE: 07711 897168
WEBSITE: BROWNSOXFORD.COM

 BROWNSOXFORD    BROWNS_OX4

Café Coco opened on Cowley Road 25 years ago; it's been winning awards and supporters ever since. Pizzas, ground steak burgers and superfood salads. A huge breakfast menu ranges from Coco Full English to Superfood Porridge. Exquisite fruit and veggie juices made to order. GF and veggie options.

WHY WE LOVE IT: GREAT TASTING FOOD IN A FUNKY SETTING, PARTICULARLY GOOD ON A SUNNY DAY WITH THE BI-FOLD DOORS SWUNG OPEN, ESPECIALLY IF YOU LIKE PEOPLE WATCHING!

ADDRESS: 23 COWLEY ROAD, OXFORD OX4 1HP
TELEPHONE: 01865 200232
WEBSITE: CAFECOCO.CO.UK

 CAFECOCOOXFORD

 CAFECOCO2

CUTTLEFISH

Cuttlefish brings the best seasonal sustainable fish to Oxford at the fairest of prices. With an extensive a la carte menu featuring oysters, lobster & seafood platters, as well as promotional dishes such as mussels with a beer, classic fish and chips with a glass of wine and a fixed price menu from 8.50.

WHY WE LOVE IT: NEW FISH ON THE BLOCK, SHOWCASING THE FRESHEST FISH AND CLASSIC BRITISH DISHES. THEIR FISH AND CHIPS IS A FAVOURITE OF OURS.

ADDRESS: 37 ST CLEMENTS, OXFORD OX4 1AB
TELEPHONE: 01865 243003
WEBSITE: CUTTLEFISHOXFORD.CO.UK

 CUTTLEFISHOXFORD    CUTTLEFISHOXFORD

Fisher Studios - Oxford's commercial photographers. We take pride in our house style and wide range of photographic services including: event, people, product, spaces, science and theatre photography. Each of our photographers draws on their unique artistic vision to create a class of product our clients can rely on.

WHY WE LOVE IT: PROFESSIONAL AND CREATIVE PHOTOS FROM A DOWN TO EARTH AND FRIENDLY TEAM.

ADDRESS: UNIT 2 THE GALLERY, 54 MARSTON STREET, OXFORD OX4 1LF
TELEPHONE: 01865 202210
WEBSITE: FISHERSTUDIOS.CO.UK

 FISHERSTUDIOSUK

INDIGO

Situated on the famous Cowley Road, Indigo offers a relaxed and friendly shopping experience. You'll find a wholesome range of men's and women's clothing, gifts and homewares, characterised by their beauty and innovation. We support sustainable business and see our community as both local and global. Come and say hello!

WHY WE LOVE IT: SARAH & JOSH HAVE BEAUTIFULLY CURATED THIS WONDERFUL SHOP ON COWLEY ROAD. FIND GORGEOUS FAIRTRADE CLOTHES AND HOMEWARES, PLUS HANDMADE JEWELLERY, AS WELL AS A WARM AND FRIENDLY WELCOME.

ADDRESS: 62 COWLEY ROAD, OXFORD OX4 1JB
TELEPHONE: 01865 794176
WEBSITE: SHOPINDIGO.CO.UK

 INDIGOOXFORD

 INDIGOOXFORD

 INDIGOOXFORD

Authentic and varied tapas menu, Sangria by the jug, Spanish wines and cocktails plus live Flamenco music make for memorable nights out. Recommended by the Sunday Times as "one of the best" with "Pork cheeks to die for!". The design is Moorish, the food is Spanish, the buzz is contagious.

WHY WE LOVE IT: BOOK A REST DAY FOR THE DAY AFTER, BECAUSE YOU'LL HAVE A HELL OF A NIGHT HERE. TASTY TAPAS AND DAMN FINE COCKTAILS IN A BUZZING VENUE

ADDRESS: 25-27 COWLEY ROAD, OXFORD OX4 1HP
TELEPHONE: 01865 202920
WEBSITE: KAZBAR.CO.UK

 KAZBAROXFORD    KAZBAROXFORD    KAZBAROXFORD

LA CUCINA

La Cucina embraces the way of Italian life! Food is foremost and served as at home in Italy! From the open kitchen you can watch chefs tossing pizza, baking foccacia, preparing ragu at the stove and all the products used throughout the day are on display. Alberto's team serve traditional hearty Italian dishes as well as great seasonal specials.

WHY WE LOVE IT: CONTEMPORARY ITALIAN TRATTORIA WITH GREAT TRADITIONAL DISHES AND SOME DIFFERENT DISHES. THEIR LUNCH DEAL IS GREAT VALUE!

ADDRESS: 39 - 40 ST CLEMENTS, OXFORD OX4 1AB
TELEPHONE: 01865 793811
WEBSITE: LACUCINAOXFORD.CO.UK

 LACUCINAOXFORD

 LACUCINA_OXFORD

The Magdalen Arms is a great gastro pub in the heart of East Oxford. The pub has a large dining room and daily changing menu, as well as a great bar area where you can relax with friends and order food at the bar. The outside area is perfect for catching the last rays of sun in the evening.

WHY WE LOVE IT: GASTROPUB WITHOUT PRETENSIONS, JUST GREAT, HEARTY, SEASONAL DISHES. GO HUNGRY!

ADDRESS: 243 IFFLEY RD, OXFORD OX4 1SJ
TELEPHONE: 01865 243159
WEBSITE: MAGDALENARMS.CO.UK

 THE-MAGDALEN-ARMS-GASTRO-PUB-OXFORD

 MAGDALEN_ARMS

SILVIE

Silvie is a bakery café in East Oxford. Baking a simple menu that strives to combine & celebrate flavour, season, tradition & creativity with a sense of community. It offers a simple and fresh approach: a friendly, no-frills, laid back escape that is a home from home.

WHY WE LOVE IT: SERVING DELICIOUS COFFEE, BREAKFAST, LUNCH AND CAKES, INCLUDING THEIR AMAZING CINNAMON BUNS. BEYOND THE CONSERVATORY IS A LOVELY SUN TRAP OF A GARDEN.

ADDRESS: 281 IFFLEY ROAD, OXFORD OX4 4AQ
TELEPHONE: 01865 246822
WEBSITE: SILVIE.CO.UK

 SILIVE

 HELLOSILVIE

 SILVIE_OX4

Annie Sloan transformed the world of furniture painting, creating her own brand of decorative paint, Chalk Paint®. She is a world renowned author and authority on decorative paint techniques. Her shop plays host to inspirational interior and homeware ideas, workshops, informative advice and the whole Annie Sloan paint and fabric range.

WHY WE LOVE IT: ANNA AND I LOVE VISITING THIS SHOP TO DISCOVER ANNIE'S LATEST VINTAGE FINDS AND UPCYCLED FURNITURE.

ADDRESS: 33 COWLEY ROAD, OXFORD OX4 1HP
TELEPHONE: 01865 247296
WEBSITE: ANNIESLOAN.COM

 THEANNIESLOANSHOP

 ANNIESLOANSHOP

 THEANNIESLOANSHOP

THE CHESTER

Freehold independent pub, restaurant, cafe & corner shop in OX4.
Home of Hamzah's famous Steak Platter.

WHY WE LOVE IT: ANOTHER OF OUR FAVOURITES, WE GO FOR THE SUNDAY
ROAST OR THAT FAMOUS STEAK PLATTER WHICH IS JUST SUBLIME. LEAVE
ROOM FOR DESSERT TOO!

ADDRESS: 19 CHESTER ST, OXFORD OX4 1SN
TELEPHONE: 01865 790438
WEBSITE:

 THECHESTEROXFORD    THECHESTEROX4

Oxford's one and only bead shop offering everything for jewellery makers of all levels. Whether you're already a jeweller, just starting out or trying to find that special gift you'll find all the workshops, supplies and personalised gifts you need in this friendly Oxford shop.

WHY WE LOVE IT: VISIT AMY TO DEVELOP YOUR JEWELLERY MAKING SKILLS! SHE IS KNOWLEDGABLE, BRILLIANT AT IMPARTING ADVICE, TOTALLY ENCOURAGING, AND ENTHUSIASTIC ABOUT HER CRAFT.

ADDRESS: 75 WILKINS ROAD, COWLEY, OXFORD OX4 2HZ
TELEPHONE: 01865 774298
WEBSITE: AMYSURMAN.COM

 THEOXFORDBEADSHOP  OXFORDBEADSHOP  OXFORDBEADS

THE ULTIMATE PICTURE PALACE

The place in Oxford for film lovers! This locally owned cinema hand picks the best of the recent releases from around the world and regularly shows old classics. No adverts, no popcorn and a bar that sells wine, local beers and homemade tasty treats. This quirky little cinema does things differently.

WHY WE LOVE IT: THIS AWESOME CINEMA SHOWS A GREAT SELECTION OF FILMS, PLUS HOUSES A BAR WITHIN THE THEATRE SO YOU CAN ENJOY A DRINK WHILE YOU SIT BACK IN ONE OF THEIR NEWLY REFURBISHED SEATS TO ENJOY YOUR FILM!

ADDRESS: JEUNE STREET, COWLEY, OXFORD OX4 1BN
TELEPHONE: 01865 245288
WEBSITE: UPPCINEMA.COM

 UPPCINEMA    UPPCINEMA   UPPCINEMA

Truck Store is a proper record shop in the heart of the music community. Driven by enthusiasm and passion for new music, Truck Store is the best place to pick up new, classic, recommended or local music, catch a live performance in-store or grab a coffee or beer in Mostro - all under the same roof!

WHY WE LOVE IT: A GREAT RECORD STORE ON COWLEY ROAD, WHICH REGULARLY HOLDS IN STORE PERFORMANCES FROM A WHOLE HOST OF ARTISTS. HAVE A COFFEE OR BEER AT MOSTRO, THEIR IN-HOUSE CAFÉ.

ADDRESS: 101 COWLEY ROAD, OXFORD OX4 1HU
TELEPHONE: 01865 793866
WEBSITE: TRUCKMUSICSTORE.CO.UK

 TRUCKSTOREOXFORD    TRUCKMUSICSTORE    TRUCKMUSICSTORE

WILD HONEY

Wild Honey is Oxford's Organic Health Store for fresh, local produce, high quality supplements, skincare & beauty, household essentials, staples & grains and heavenly snacks & treats! We are a family-run business, passionate about health, and deeply committed to the well-being of our community in Oxford.

WHY WE LOVE IT: AN INSTANT HIT WHEN THEY OPENED ON MAGDALEN ROAD AND NOW HAVE A SECOND STORE ON SOUTH PARADE, SUMMERTOWN. THEY RECENTLY WON UK INDEPENDENT HEALTH FOOD SHOP OF THE YEAR!

ADDRESS: 111 MAGDALEN ROAD OX4 1RQ & 12 SOUTH PARADE OX2 7JL
TELEPHONE: 01865 803724
WEBSITE: WILDHONEYLOVE.COM

 WILDHONEYHEALTH    WILDHONEYLOVE    WILDHONEYLOVE

Our passion and our art is your hair. We want to welcome you to something different, to relaxation, enjoyment, a fresh look and a new you. We only use animal cruelty free and sulphate free products and offer discounts for students, NHS and Oxfam staff.

WHY WE LOVE IT: A STYLISH NEW HAIRDRESSERS ON COWLEY ROAD. OUR FRIEND JANE FROM BICYCLE BLOOMS RATES ŽANETA'S SALON HIGHLY AND WE THINK HER HAIR SURE LOOKS GREAT!

ADDRESS: 181 COWLEY ROAD, OXFORD OX4 1UT
TELEPHONE: 01865 240642
WEBSITE: ZLSALON.CO.UK

 ZLSALON    KEVIN.MURPHY_ZLSALON

INDIE
PEOPLE

BERNARD IWO PHOTOGRAPHY

Oxford photographer available for your event needs. From weddings, parties and bar mitzvahs to food events, street photography and videos, I specialise in unposed images. Resident photographer at #BittenStreet street food market.

TELEPHONE: 07720 263050
WEBSITE: BERNARDIWO.COM

BECKY MORGANS JEWELLERY

Handmade, contemporary silver & gold jewellery designer/maker. Becky's work explores & emphasises contrast in metal, using gold, oxidised silver, texture & adds colour to her work by using sea glass stones & fresh water pearls.

TELEPHONE: 07773 018984
WEBSITE: BECKYJEWELLERY.COM

 BECKYJEWELLERY    BECKYMORGANS_JEWELLERY

ERMANA NATURAL SKINCARE

Ermana is a natural skincare range of face and body oils and balms which are made from a rich blend of plant oils and butters. All our products are hand blended locally in Oxfordshire and are packed with essential vitamins and minerals.

TELEPHONE: 07765 896586
WEBSITE: ERMANA.CO.UK

    ERMAMASKINCARE    ERMANASKINCARE

HAPPY CAKES

Pimped up Mega Cupcakes and Baby Cakes made with fun and love from our Summertown kitchen. A regular at #BittenStreet every month.

TELEPHONE: 07814 519611
WEBSITE: HAPPY-CAKES.CO.UK

 HAPPYCAKESUK    HAPPYCAKESUK    HAPPYCAKESUK

The lifestyle store where everything's Rosie! A colourful and fun collection of gifts curated by Rosie Jacobs (also one half of Independent Oxford!) including jewellery, accessories, homeware and stationery.

WHY WE LOVE IT: NIRVANA FOR THOSE WHO LIKE UNUSUAL ACCESSORIES, JEWELLERY, STATIONERY, HOME FURNISHINGS AND POMPOMS! IF YOU NEED A GIFT FOR SOMEONE OR WANT TO TREAT YOURSELF, THIS IS THE PERFECT PLACE TO SHOP

WEBSITE: AROSIELIFE.CO.UK

 ROSIELIFESTORE

 ROSIELIFESTORE

 ROSIELIFESTORE

BOUNCE

The Bounce shop isn't just a shop, it's a design studio too. We take pride in being a family business. Visit for a professional graphic design service, or to browse our unique range of gifts, art prints and t-shirts/hoodies - all printed here at Bounce, with art from local artists! We also print large format posters and vinyl stickers.

WHY WE LOVE IT: SEAN & JOE HAVE BEEN SUPPORTIVE OF THE INDIE OXFORD COMPENDIUM PROJECT AND HAVE HELPED US ACHIEVE THE CREATION OF THIS AWESOME BOOK. IT'S BEEN GREAT TO WORK WITH THIS OX4 BASED INDIE TEAM.

ADDRESS: 101 MAGDALEN RD, OXFORD OX4 1RG
TELEPHONE: 01865 200123
WEBSITE: BOUNCEDESIGN.CO.UK

 BOUNCEDESIGNUK

 BOUNCEDESIGNUK

 DESIGNBOUNCE

Cultivate is a cooperative organisation owned and funded by the community dedicated to creating a better food system for Oxford. We work with local growers, farmers and producers to bring the best organic, ethical and delicious fresh produce to the people of Oxford. Find us around the city in our VegVan and market stalls.

WHY WE LOVE IT: SUPPLYING BRILLIANT LOCAL PRODUCE ONE STOP AT A TIME, MEANING YOU GET THE FRESHEST PRODUCE WITHOUT THE ADDED FOOD MILES AND WHILE ALSO SUPPORTING LOCAL PRODUCERS.

ADDRESS: WEEKLY STOPS IN BOTLEY, COWLEY, HEADINGTON, JERICHO AND SUMMERTOWN. CHECK THE WEBSITE FOR DETAILS

WEBSITE: CULTIVATEOXFORD.ORG

 CULTIVATEOXFORD

 CULTIVATEOXFORD

JERICHO STUDIO POTTERY

Artisan studio pottery with a focus on function and simple beauty. Handmade tableware, thrown on the wheel in durable stoneware with a relaxed, unfussy look. Each piece is unique. All work is created by Hannah Jervis and can be viewed in her Oxford studio, which you are welcome to visit by arrangement.

WHY WE LOVE IT: HANNAH HAS BEEN IMMENSELY SUPPORTIVE OF INDEPENDENT OXFORD SINCE THE START AND WE LOVE HER POTTERY AND HER PASSION FOR THE CRAFT.

WEBSITE: JERICHOSTUDIOPOTTERY.COM

 JERICHOSTUDIOPOTTERY  JERICHOSTUDIOPOTTERY

Merrie & Bright Calligraphy specialises in creating elegant and whimsical hand-lettered details for home decor, gifts, weddings and events and more! Designing and creating stunning pieces from her studio in Oxfordshire, Merrie is passionate about creating beauty through her work and products.

WHY WE LOVE IT: MERRIE IS AN ACTIVE MEMBER OF OUR INDEPENDENT OXFORD COMMUNITY AND WE HAVE LOVED SEEING HER DEVELOP HER SKILLS AND HER BEAUTIFUL RANGE OVER THE LAST YEAR.

WEBSITE: MERRIEANDBRIGHT.COM

 MERRIEANDBRIGHT

 MERRIE.AND.BRIGHT

NC OXFORD CANDLES

NC Oxford is Oxfordshire's premier producer of luxury natural wax scented candles, tea lights and reed diffusers. All of our products are hand-poured in our Oxfordshire workshop close to the historic town of Woodstock. Elegant design, combined with the highest quality produce makes an NC Oxford product a great addition to any room.

WHY WE LOVE IT: I HAVE THE SIR WINSTON DIFFUSER IN MY OFFICE AND IT SMELLS AMAZING EVERY DAY. THEIR OXFORD THEMED SCENTS ARE PERFECT AS GIFTS AND LAST FOR AGES.

ADDRESS: SUITE 221, 266 BANBURY ROAD, OXFORD, OX2 7DL
TELEPHONE: 01865 703055
WEBSITE: NCOXFORD.COM

 NCOXFORD

 NC_OXFORD

 NCOXFORD

We are a small but perfectly formed children's home decor brand called Red Hand Gang. We design, make and hand screen print a whole range of gorgeous goodies for kids rooms and it is all made in our workshop in Oxford!

WHY WE LOVE IT: ABI'S BEAUTIFUL RANGE OF FUN HOMEWARES FOR KIDS, MAKE GREAT GIFTS AND ADDITIONS TO YOUR HOME.

TELEPHONE: 07765 636275
WEBSITE: REDHANDGANG.CO.UK

 MYREDHANDGANG

INDIE
EVENTS

Oxford's monthly street food market with the best local and visiting street food crews. You can also expect a bar stocked with great local craft beers, cider, and house cocktails, plus music from resident DJ Ollie East, all in the beautiful setting of Oxford Castle Quarter. First Saturday monthly from 11am - 3pm, March till September.

WHY WE LOVE IT: NOT JUST YOUR AVERAGE STREET FOOD, THE PROPER GOOD STUFF! THE LINE-UP IS DIFFERENT EVERY MONTH TOO, SO YOU'LL NEVER GET BORED. TOP TIP: TAKE A SHARING BUDDY SO YOU CAN TRY MORE!

ADDRESS: OXFORD CASTLE QUARTER, OXFORD, OX1 1AY
WEBSITE: BITTENSTREET.COM

 BITTENOXFORD

 BITTENOXFORD

 BITTENOXFORD

INDEPENDENT OXFORD CHRISTMAS MARKET

Join us for our 3rd Independent Oxford Christmas Market! We've got a whole host of wonderful indies and designer makers awaiting you. Plus join us for a workshop, relax with a cup of tea and don't forget to enter our awesome prize draw to bag yourself a fabulous goody bag of treats from our talented stall holders.

WHY WE LOVE IT: WE'RE EXCITED TO BRING YOU OUR 3RD CHRISTMAS MARKET! IT'S A GREAT SHOWCASE OF OUR FAVOURITE INDIES AND MAKERS UNDER ONE ROOF AND A BRILLIANT WAY TO HELP YOU SHOP LOCALLY AT CHRISTMAS.

WEBSITE: INDEPENDENTOXFORD.COM/EVENTS

 INDEPENDENTOXFORD    INDIEOXFORD    INDEPENDENTOXFORD

With the sound of choirs singing Christmas carols, market traders offering unique gifts, and the aroma of mulled wine and cinnamon drifting in the air - a visit to the annual Oxford Christmas Market is a truly magical Christmas experience. Est. in 2009 by Nicole Rahimi, the event has become a Christmas tradition for many from near and far.

WHY WE LOVE IT: THE OXFORD CHRISTMAS MARKET IS A LOVELY GERMAN STYLE MARKET WITH A GREAT SELECTION OF STALLS AND PERFORMANCES HELPING YOU TO KICK OFF YOUR CHRISTMAS SHOPPING AND EMBRACE THE FESTIVE SPIRIT!

TELEPHONE: 07910 342748
WEBSITE: OXFORDCHRISTMASMARKET.CO.UK

 OXFORDXMASMARKET    OXFORDCHRISTMAS    OXFORDXMASMARKET

OXFORD FOOD & DRINK FESTIVAL

Oxford's very own food & drink festival, featuring local businesses and producers, all based within a maximum of 1 hours drive of Oxford. Run by Jacqui & Becca from Bitten Oxford, the bustling festival launched in 2016 filling the city centre with people and glorious food smells.

WHY WE LOVE IT: THERE ARE SO MANY FOOD FESTIVALS AROUND US BUT NONE EXCLUSIVELY FOCUSED ON LOCAL BUSINESSES. THIS FESTIVAL CELEBRATES ALL THE AMAZING FOOD AND DRINK THERE IS ON OUR DOORSTEP.

ADDRESS: OXFORD UNIVERSITY PARKS, OXFORD
WEBSITE: OXFOODFEST.COM

 OXFOODFEST

 OXFOODFEST

 OXFOODFEST

INDEX

INDEX